DINOSAUR PLAY SCHOOL

Have fun with Colours, Counting, ABC and Time

Illustrated by Jan Lewis

Once upon a time
there was a big brown egg.
It cracked down the middle
And out came a leg.

One little
dinosaur
Red, red, red!

Out came a tail,
Out came a head...

Red dinosaur was hungry.
What could he find to eat?
Fresh green leaves and
flower buds
were a real dinosaur treat!

Red dinosaur was lonely,
Where could he find
a friend?

A herd of great grey
dinosaurs
was just around the bend.

One little grey dinosaur
wanted to stay and play,
so he hid behind a big
black rock...

as the herd went on
its way.

The dinosaurs went paddling in the blue, blue sea... and ran across the yellow sand as happy as can be.

They heard somebody snoring
And when they looked around...

They saw an orange dinosaur sleeping on the ground.

They woke the orange dinosaur who took them off to see...

A place where pink and purple flowers covered every tree.

They met a big white
pterosaur
who said,
"Let's play a game...

"How many colours can you name?"

brown

red

green

grey

white

black

blue

yellow

orange

pink

purple

1 One huge dinosaur going for a walk.

2 Two tiny dinosaurs stop to talk.

3 Three tall
dinosaurs
munching
in the trees.

4 Four dinosaurs
with horns
and knobbly
knees.

5 Five frisky dinosaurs having lots of fun.

6 Six spiky dinosaurs standing in the Sun.

7 Seven mummy dinosaurs looking after eggs.

8 Eight daddy dinosaurs with very long legs.

9 Nine hungry dinosaurs hunting for tea.

10 Ten terrible Tyrannosaurs

chasing after me!

Can you count...

1 silly dinosaur

2 eyes

3 tail spikes

4 legs

5 flowers

6 leaves

7 stripes

8 spots

9 eggs

10 teeth

A is for Apatosaurus and apple.

B is for Baryonyx and bat.

C is for Carnotaurus and claw.

H is for Hadrosaurus and hedge.

G is for Gallimimus and grass.

I is for Iguanodon and insect.

K is for
Kentrosaurus
and kite.

J is for
Jubbulpuria
and jug.

L is for
Leptoceratops
and ladder.

N is for Nodosaurus and nuts.

M is for Monoclonius and melons.

O is for Oviraptor and oranges.

Q is for Quaesitosaurus and quilt.

P is for Protoceratops and pillow.

R is for Riojasaurus and rainbow.

S is for Stegosaurus and sun.

T is for Tyrannosaurus and tree.

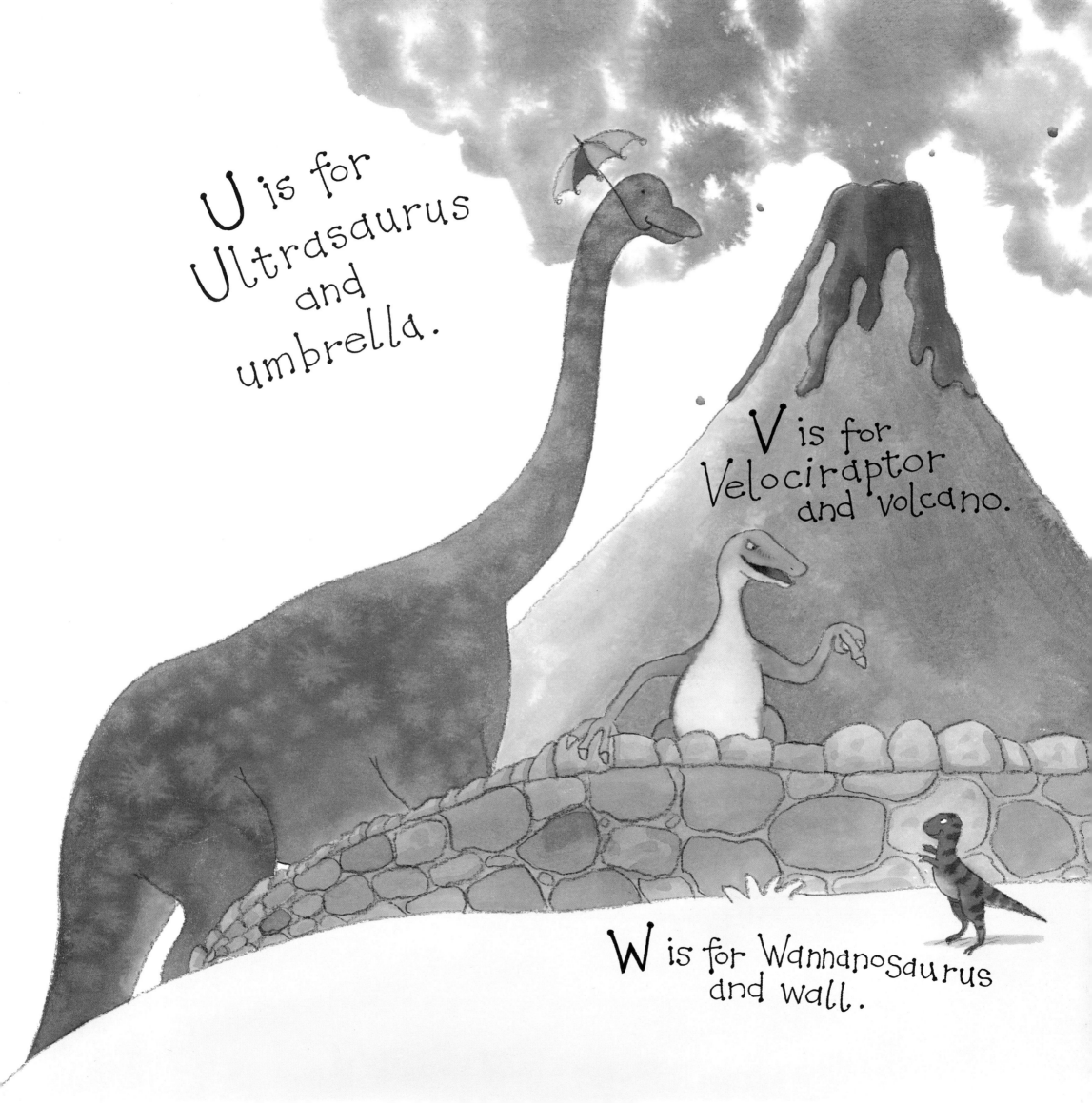

U is for Ultrasaurus and umbrella.

V is for Velociraptor and volcano.

W is for Wannanosaurus and wall.

Y is for Yunnanosaurus and yoyo.

X is for Xiaosaurus and xylophone.

Z is for Zephyrosaurus and zigzag.

Can you say all these dinosaur names?

A   Apatosaurus say it, "a-pat-o-saw-rus"

B   Baryonyx say it, "ba-ree-on-ix"

C   Carnotaurus say it, "car-no-tor-rus"

D   Diplodocus say it, "dip-lo-doh-kus"

E   Edmontosaurus say it, "ed-mon-toe-saw-rus"

F   Fabrosaurus say it, "fab-ro-saw-rus"

G   Gallimimus say it, "gal-lee-my-mus"

H   Hadrosaurus say it, "had-ro-saw-rus"

I   Iguanodon say it, "ig-wah-no-don"

J   Jubbulpuria say it, "jub-bull-paw-ree-a"

K   Kentrosaurus say it, "ken-tro-saw-rus"

L   Leptoceratops say it, "lep-toe-serra-tops"

M   Monoclonius say it, "mon-o-klo-nee-us"

N   Nodosaurus say it, "no-doh-saw-rus"

O   Oviraptor say it, "o-ve-rap-tor"

P   Protoceratops say it, "pro-to-serra-tops"

Q   Quaesitosaurus say it, "kee-sit-o-saw-rus"

R   Riojasaurus say it, "ree-ock-a-saw-rus"

S   Stegosaurus say it, "steg-o-saw-rus"

T   Tyrannosaurus say it, "ti-ran-no-saw-rus"

U   Ultrasaurus say it, "ull-tra-saw-rus"

V   Velociraptor say it, "vel-o-si-rap-tor"

W   Wannanosaurus say it, "wa-nan-o-saw-rus"

X   Xiaosaurus say it, "zwow-saw-rus"

Y   Yunnanosaurus say it, "you-nan-o-saw-rus"

Z   Zephyrosaurus say it, "zef-er-ro-saw-rus"

By 10 o'clock they know
all seven days for sure.
"What comes after Wednesday?"
"Thursday!" the dinos roar.

When the clock strikes 11
they stop for a snack.
Then the bell rings out loudly
and they all hurry back.

Sunda
Mond
Tue

Milk

The Found World

At 12 o'clock it's time
to learn something new.
All about the seasons
and the twelve months too.

Spring

Summer

Autumn

Winter

January

February

March

July

June

May

August

September

October

November

December

April

1 o'clock means
it's now time for lunch.
The dinosaurs are hungry
so they gobble, chew,
and munch!

After lunch it's playtime.
The dinosaurs chase and shout.
When the whistle blows at 2 o'clock
Little Dinosaur's tired out!

Painting follows playtime
and lasts for one whole hour.
By 3 o'clock Little Dinosaur
has drawn a lovely flower.

The clock strikes 4.
It's the end of the day.
The dinosaurs hurry home
running all the way.

When 5 o'clock comes
it's time for a treat!
Chocolate cake and ice cream—
There's plenty to eat.

6 o'clock is bathtime –
Dinosaurs jump in the tub.
Don't forget to wash your face
and give your tail a scrub!

What's your favourite time of day?

 **07.00**
Seven o'clock in the morning.
"When I get up."

 **08.00**
Eight o'clock
"When I have my breakfast."

 **09.00**
Nine o'clock
"When I go to school."

 **10.00**
Ten o'clock
"When I do lessons."

 **11.00**
Eleven o'clock
"When it's time for a snack."

 **12.00**
Twelve o'clock
"When we learn new things."

 **13.00**
One o'clock
"When I eat lunch."

 **14.00**
Two o'clock
"When playtime ends."

 **15.00**
Three o'clock
"When I paint a picture."

 **16.00**
Four o'clock
""When school is over."

 **17.00**
Five o'clock
"When there are treats to eat."

 **18.00**
Six o'clock
"When I splash in the bath."

 **19.00**
Seven o'clock in the evening.
"When I go to bed."

 **20.00**
Eight o'clock

 21.00
Nine o'clock

 22.00
Ten o'clock

 23.00
Eleven o'clock

 24.00
Twelve o'clock

 01.00
One o'clock

 02.00
Two o'clock

 **03.00**
Three o'clock

 04.00
Four o'clock

 **05.00**
Five o'clock

06.00
Six o'clock